FACES AND PLACES
POEMS FOR YOU

Selected by Lee Bennett Hopkins
and Misha Arenstein

Illustrated by Lisl Weil

SCHOLASTIC BOOK SERVICES

NEW YORK · TORONTO · LONDON · AUCKLAND · SYDNEY · TOKYO

ISBN: 0-590-04708-6

13 12 11 10 9 8 7 6 5   9/7 0 1 2 3 4/8

Printed in the U. S. A.   11

For reprint permission grateful acknowledgment is made to the following:

Richard Armour for "Money" from AN ARMOURY OF LIGHT VERSE by Richard
Armour, copyright 1964 by Bruce Humphries.

Atheneum Publishers for "The Travelers" by Patricia Hubbell, copyright © 1963
by Patricia Hubbell, from THE APPLE VENDOR'S FAIR; "Message from a Mouse
Ascending in a Rocket" by Patricia Hubbell, copyright © 1968 by Patricia
Hubbell, from CATCH ME A WIND; "Wrestling," "Tug of War," and "Tree
Climbing" by Kathleen Fraser, copyright © 1968 by Kathleen Fraser, from
STILTS, SOMERSAULTS, AND HEADSTANDS; "Leavetaking" by Eve Merriam,
copyright © 1964 by Eve Merriam, from IT DOESN'T ALWAYS HAVE TO
RHYME; "A Lazy Thought" and "Conversation" by Eve Merriam, copyright ©
1962 by Eve Merriam, from THERE IS NO RHYME FOR SILVER; "Shells,"
"Reflections," and "Foghorns," text copyright © 1969 by Lilian Moore, from
I THOUGHT I HEARD THE CITY.

Brandt & Brandt for "Western Wagons" by Stephen Vincent Benét from A BOOK
OF AMERICANS by Rosemary and Stephen Vincent Benét, published by Holt,
Rinehart and Winston, Inc., copyright 1933 by Rosemary and Stephen Vincent
Benét, copyright renewed © 1961 by Rosemary Carr Benét.

The Bruce Publishing Co., for lines from "The Math Battle" by Stephen Silberam
from YOUNG VOICES, poetry by New York City children, compiled by Schaefer
and Mellor, © 1971 by the Center for Urban Education, New York.

The Christian Science Publishing Society for "Post Early For Space" by Peter J.
Henniker-Heaton from The Christian Science Monitor, © 1952 the Christian
Science Publishing Society.

William Cole for "It's such a shock" from RHYME GIGGLES by William Cole;
"Valentine" by Shel Silverstein, © 1961 by Shel Silverstein from POEMS FOR
SEASONS AND CELEBRATIONS, edited by William Cole, published by World
Publishing Co.

Crown Publishers, Inc., for "Adventure House" and "Get 'em Here" by Lee
Bennett Hopkins from THIS STREET'S FOR ME! Text copyright © 1970 by Lee
Bennett Hopkins.

Doubleday & Co., Inc., for "On a Journey" by Bashō and "The Dragonfly" by
Chisoku from AN INTRODUCTION TO HAIKU by Harold G. Henderson, copyright © 1958 by Harold G. Henderson; and "December" by Sanderson Vanderbilt from CREATIVE YOUTH, edited by Hughes Mearns. Copyright 1925 by
Doubleday & Co., Inc.

E. P. Dutton & Co., Inc. for "Wheels" from the book POEMS OF EARTH AND
SPACE by Claudia Lewis, copyright © 1967 by Claudia Lewis.

Contents

DIFFERENT FACES

Conversation

"Buenos días," says Señor Rías.
"Bonjour," says Monsieur Dutour.
"Buon giorno," says Signor Tiorno.
"Hello," says Mister Coe.

"Buenas noches," says Señora Rochas.
"Bonne nuit," says Madame La Brie.
"Buona notte," says Signora Capolotte.
"Good night," says Mrs. White.

"Hasta luego," says Señorita Diego.
"Au revoir," says Mademoiselle Loire.
"Arrivederci," says Signorina Terci.
"See you soon," says Miss Calhoun.

EVE MERRIAM

Reflections

On this street
of windowed stores
see,
in the glass
shadow people meet
and pass
and glide to
secret places.

Ghostly mothers
hold
the hands of dim gray children,
scold
them silently
and melt away.

And ―
now and then,
before
the window mirror
of a store,
phantom faces
stop
and window shop.

LILIAN MOORE

Hokku: In the Falling Snow

In the falling snow
A laughing boy holds out his palms
Until they are white

RICHARD WRIGHT

December

A little boy stood on the corner
And shoveled bits of dirty, soggy snow
Into the sewer —
With a jagged piece of tin.

He was helping spring come.

SANDERSON VANDERBILT

A Lazy Thought

There go the grownups
To the office,
To the store.
Subway rush,
Traffic crush;
Hurry, scurry,
Worry, flurry.

No wonder
Grownups
Don't grow up
Any more.

It takes a lot
Of slow
To grow.

EVE MERRIAM

Jim

There never was a nicer boy
Than Mrs. Jackson's Jim.
The sun should drop its greatest gold
On him.

Because, when Mother-dear was sick,
He brought her cocoa in.
And brought her broth, and brought her bread.
And brought her medicine.

And, tipping, tidied up her room.
And would not let her see
He missed his game of baseball
Terribly.

GWENDOLYN BROOKS

Mother to Son

Well, son, I'll tell you:
Life for me ain't been no crystal stair.
It's had tacks in it,
And splinters,
And boards torn up,
And places with no carpet on the floor —
Bare.
But all the time
I'se been a-climbin' on,
And reachin' landin's,
And turnin' corners,
And sometimes goin' in the dark
Where there ain't been no light.
So, boy, don't you turn back.
Don't you set down on the steps
'Cause you find it kinder hard.
Don't you fall now —
For I'se still goin', honey,
I'se still climbin',
And life for me ain't been no crystal stair.

LANGSTON HUGHES

Young Woman
At a Window

She sits with
tears on

her cheek
her cheek on

her hand
the child

in her lap
his nose

pressed
to the glass

WILLIAM CARLOS WILLIAMS

Kansas Boy

This Kansas boy who never saw the sea
Walks through the young corn rippling at his knee
As sailors walk; and when the grain grows higher
Watches the dark waves leap with greener fire
Than ever oceans hold. He follows ships,
Tasting the bitter spray upon his lips,
For in his blood up-stirs the salty ghost
Of one who sailed a storm-bound English coast.
Across wide fields he hears the sea winds crying,
Shouts at the crows — and dreams of white
   gulls flying.

RUTH LECHLITNER.

Portrait by a Neighbor

Before she has her floor swept
   Or her dishes done,
Any day you'll find her
   A-sunning in the sun!

It's long after midnight
   Her key's in the lock,
And you never see her chimney smoke
   Till past ten o'clock!

She digs in her garden
   With a shovel and a spoon,
She weeds her lazy lettuce
   By the light of the moon.

She walks up the walk
   Like a woman in a dream,
She forgets she borrowed butter
   And pays you back cream!

Her lawn looks like a meadow,
   And if she mows the place
She leaves the clover standing
   And the Queen Anne's lace!

EDNA ST. VINCENT MILLAY

Circles

The white man drew a small circle in the sand
     and told the red man,
"This is what the Indian knows."
And drawing a big circle around the small one,
"This is what the white man knows."

The Indian took the stick
And swept an immense ring around both circles:
"This is where the white man and the red man
     know nothing."

CARL SANDBURG

DIFFERENT PLACES

Where Are You Now?

When the night begins to fall
And the sky begins to glow
You look up and see the tall
City of light begin to grow —
In rows and little golden squares
The lights come out. First here, then there
Behind the windowpanes as though
A million billion bees had built
Their golden hives and honeycombs
Above you in the air.

MARY BRITTON MILLER

Water-Front Streets

The spring is not so beautiful there —
  But dream ships sail away
To where the spring is wondrous rare
  And life is gay.

The spring is not so beautiful there —
  But lads put out to sea
Who carry beauties in their hearts
  And dreams, like me.

LANGSTON HUGHES

Foghorns

The foghorns moaned
    in the bay last night
  so sad
  so deep
I thought I heard the city
    crying in its sleep.

LILIAN MOORE

The River Is a Piece of Sky

From the top of a bridge
The river below
Is a piece of sky —

       – Until you throw
       – A penny in
       – Or a cockleshell
       – Or a pebble or two
       – Or a bicycle bell
       – Or a cobblestone
       – Or a fat man's cane —

And then you can see
It's a river again.

The difference you'll see
When you drop your penny:
The river has splashes,
The sky hasn't any.

JOHN CIARDI

Idaho

Farmers out in Idaho
Plant potatoes, row on row.
Then before the green vines show
Every farmer has to go
Daily hoe-ing with his hoe
Up and down the rows till — lo —
Finally potatoes grow.

This, potato farmers know:
What comes up must start below;
What you reap you have to sow;
What you grow you have to hoe.

If you don't like farming, though,
And you've never *tried* a hoe
Or you hate to guide a hoe
Or you can't abide a hoe
Stay away from Idaho.

KAYE STARBIRD

Emma's Store

The store we like best is Emma's store.
It hasn't any revolving door.

It hasn't a floorman neat and polite:
"Third floor, Modom, and turn to your right."

No elevators go up and down it.
Nothing's the way it is downtown. It

Hasn't a special place for dresses;
Everything's jumbled in cozy messes —

Washcloths and lamp shades, paper dolls, slippers,
Candy and shoestrings, umbrellas and zippers;

No matter what's needed or how great the hurry
As long as there's Emma's, you don't need to worry,

And *she* never minds how long you stay.
"Why sure, take your time, dear" Emma will say.

DOROTHY ALDIS

Until We Built a Cabin

When we lived in a city
(three flights up and down)
I never dreamed how many stars
could show above a town.

When we moved to a village
where lighted streets were few.
I thought I could see ALL the stars,
but, oh, I never knew —

Until we built a cabin
where hills are high and far,
I never knew how many
          many
             stars there really are!

AILEEN FISHER

FAVORITE THINGS / FAVORITE TIMES

The Box

I've taken it down
From the high shelf;
The box marked OLD TOYS:
    A silly stuffed chicken with a missing eye,
    A farmhouse painted red with a spotted cow,
    A set of blocks and a ball made of fuzz,
    A puzzle with only five pieces,
    A giraffe with a bent neck.

Why did I play with those old things, anyway?

MYRA COHN LIVINGSTON

Shells

The bones of the sea
are on the shore,
shells
curled into the sand,
shells
caught in green weed hair.
All day I gather them
and there are always
more.

I take them home,
magic bones of the sea,
and when
I touch one,
then I hear
I taste
I smell the sea
again.

LILIAN MOORE

Tree Climbing

This is my tree,
my place to be alone in,
my branches for climbing,
my green leaves for hiding in,
my sunshine for reading,
my clouds for dreaming,
my sky for singing,
my tree, my beautiful tree.

KATHLEEN FRASER

Wilderness Rivers

There are rivers
That I know,
Born of ice
And melting snow,
White with rapids,
Swift to roar,
With no farms
Along their shore,
With no cattle
Come to drink
At a staid
And welcoming brink,
With no millwheel
Ever turning
In that cold,
Relentless churning.

Only deer
And bear and mink

At those shallows
Come to drink;
Only paddles
Swift and light
Flick that current
In their flight.
I have felt
My heart beat high,
Watching
With exultant eye
Those pure rivers
Which have known
No will, no purpose
But their own.

ELIZABETH COATSWORTH

Leavetaking

Vacation is over;
It's time to depart.
I must leave behind
(although it breaks my heart)

Tadpoles in the pond,
A can of eels,
A leaky rowboat,
Abandoned car wheels;

For I'm packing only
Necessities:
A month of sunsets
And two apple trees.

EVE MERRIAM

Adventure House

Dark!
Cool!
Mysterious!
Lights flicker here and there!
Still — except for strange voices!
A smell of its very own!
An island in the middle of the city's block!
This . . .
    is my movie house!

LEE BENNETT HOPKINS

This Is Just to Say

I have eaten
the plums
that were in
the icebox

and which
you were probably
saving
for breakfast

Forgive me
they were delicious
so sweet
and so cold.

WILLIAM CARLOS WILLIAMS

Get 'em Here

"Hot dogs with sauerkraut
Cold drinks here!
Hot dogs with sauerkraut
Get 'em here!
Hot dogs with sauerkraut
Cold drinks here!"

Shouts the man as he rolls the city's smallest
    store
All tucked neatly under a huge, blue-and-
    orange-striped-umbrella.

LEE BENNETT HOPKINS

The Winning of the TV West

When twilight comes to Prairie Street
On every TV channel,
The kids watch men with blazing guns
In jeans and checkered flannel.
Partner, the West is wild tonight —
There's going to be a battle
Between the sheriff's posse and
The gang that stole the cattle.
On every screen on Prairie Street
The sheriff roars his order:
"We've got to head those hombres off
Before they reach the border."
Clippoty-clop and bangity-bang
The lead flies left and right.
Paradise Valley is freed again
Until tomorrow night.
And all the kids on Prairie Street
Over and under ten
Can safely go to dinner now . . .
The West is won again.

JOHN T. ALEXANDER

Slumber Party

My sister had a slumber party.
Girls giggled and ate till almost dawn.
They did not sleep nor did they slumber.
So why call it a slumber party?
When they just giggled and ate the whole night long.

CARSON MCCULLERS

SPORTS AND GAMES

Tug of War

No one is quite sure
how to win at Tug of War
except that you pull
and pullll   and pulllllll
and just as you're sure
you are winning,
the other team pulls
and pulllls   and pulllllllls
and you fall their way
and then they fall your way
but
if everyone on your team
should suddenly take a big breath
and tug all together
with arms around each other
then you might just possibly win.

KATHLEEN FRASER

Fielder's Chatter:
The Little League Game

That's no hitter!
That's no batter!
That's no runner, Drew.
Pitch that ball
Across the plate.
That batter's scared of you!
You can do it!
Nothing to it!
Easy does it.
He's OUT!

BOBBI KATZ

Baseball.
Tension-filled sport,
When the pitcher winds up,
And the batter swings and misses . . .
Action!

JOEL WAGNER

The Base Stealer

Poised between going on and back, pulled
Both ways taut like a tightrope-walker,
Fingertips pointing the opposites,
Now bouncing tiptoe like a dropped ball
Or a kid skipping rope, come on, come on,
Running a scattering of steps sidewise,
How he teeters, skitters, tingles, teases,
Taunts them, hovers like an ecstatic bird,
He's only flirting, crowd him, crowd him,
Delicate, delicate, delicate, delicate — now!

ROBERT FRANCIS

Foul Shot

With two 60's stuck on the scoreboard
And two seconds hanging on the clock,
The solemn boy in the center of eyes,
Squeezed by silence,
Seeks out the line with his feet,
Soothes his hands along his uniform,
Gently drums the ball against the floor
Then measures the waiting net,
Raises the ball on his right hand,
Balances it with his left,
Calms it with fingertips,
Breathes,
Crouches,
Waits,
And then through a stretching of stillness,
Nudges it upward.

The ball
Slides up and out,
Lands,
Leans,
Wobbles,
Wavers,
Hesitates,
Exasperates,
Plays it coy
Until every face begs with unsounding screams —

And then,

           And then

                And then,

Right before ROAR-UP,
Dives down and through.

EDWIN A. HOEY

Wrestling

I like wrestling with Herbie because
he's my best friend.
We poke each other
(but not very hard)
and punch each other
(but not very hard)
and roll on the grass
and pretend to have fights
just to make our sisters scream.
But sometimes if he hits me too much
and it hurts,
I get mad
and I punch him back
as hard as I can
and then we both are crying
and going into our houses

and slamming our back doors on each other.
But the next day, if it's sunny,
we come out into our yards
and grin at each other,
and sometimes he gives me an apple
or I give him a cookie and
then we start wrestling again.

KATHLEEN FRASER

Chair Lift

Nobody holds your hand up there.
You sit alone in your moving chair.

It's not as smooth as an elevator.
It's scarier than an escalator.

Under your feet, the snowy humps
Of hills go by with jerks and bumps

And the only sound in the world is the clack
Of the chair lift clanking along its track.

The trees move past in a stiff parade
Like ice cream cones that giants made.

And suddenly, you're not a king.
You're not the head of anything.

Your feet are cold, your nose is runny,
Your stomach flutters and feels funny,

You wish the whole machine would stop
— And then, with a whir, you're off at the top.

MAXINE W. KUMIN

Skiing

Skiing is like being
part of a mountain.
On the early morning run
before the crowds begin,
my skiis make
    little blizzards
as they plough
    through untouched powder
to leave fresh tracks
    in the blue-white snow.
My body bends and turns
    to catch each
bend and turn
    the mountain takes;
and I am the mountain
and the mountain is me.

BOBBI KATZ

O Beautiful Here

O beautiful here, water
Bubbles on clear foam,
Warming to the sun at top,
Shivery to bone:
Floating in cool nothingness
Blue pool waters brim:
O beautiful here, water
Weightless, I swim.

MYRA COHN LIVINGSTON

Song for a Surf-Rider

I ride the horse that is the sea.
His mane of foam flows wild and free.
His eyes flash with an emerald fire.
His mighty heart will never tire.
His hoofbeats echo on the sand.
He quivers as I raise my hand.
We race together, the sea and I,
Under the watching summer sky
To where the magic islands lie.

SARA VAN ALSTYNE ALLEN

FROM HERE TO THERE

Taking Off

The airplane taxis down the field
And heads into the breeze,
It lifts its wheels above the ground,
It skims above the trees,
It rises high and higher
Away up toward the sun,
It's just a speck against the sky
— And now it's gone!

ANONYMOUS

Western Wagons

They went with axe and rifle,
    when the trail was still to blaze,
They went with wife and children,
    in the prairie schooner days,
With banjo and with frying pan —
    Susanna, don't you cry!
For I'm off to California
    to get rich out there or die!

We've broken land and cleared it,
    but we're tired of where we are.
They say that wild Nebraska
    is a better place by far.
There's gold in far Wyoming,
    there's black earth in Ioway,
So pack up the kids and blankets,
    for we're moving out today!

The cowards never started
    and the weak died on the road,
And all across the continent
    the endless campfires glowed.
We'd taken land and settled
    — but a traveler passed by —
And we're going West tomorrow —
    Lordy, never ask us why!

We're going West tomorrow,
    where the promises can't fail.
O'er the hills in legions, boys,
    and crowd the dusty trail!
We shall starve and freeze and suffer.
    We shall die, and tame the lands.
But we're going West tomorrow,
    with our fortune in our hands.

STEPHEN VINCENT BENÉT

Wheels

Wheels over the mountains
Wheels over the plains —
Covered wagon wheels
In the winds and the rains

Marked the path
Of the pioneers
Across our land
In the early years.

Straight through the wilderness
Westward bound
The wagons moved on,
Breaking new ground.

And now, far above
That ancient trail
Carved by the wheels
The jet planes sail.

From the eastern shore
To the west they flow
And they skim in half a day
All the continent below.

And where are their wheels?
Tucked inside,
With nothing to do
 But ride and ride

Across those miles
That were hard and slow
For the covered wagons
Of long ago.

CLAUDIA LEWIS

Sea way!
Boats floating by
They go many places
I wish I could go somewhere far
Away.

SYLVIA BRIODY

River Night

Up and down the river
The barges go:
Whether moons are yellow,
Whether stars flow
Softly over city,
Softly over town,
Sleepily the barges
Go up and down.

Up and down the river
On summer nights
The barges drift,
And emerald lights
And crimson prick
The darkness under
Blown-out stars
And gathering thunder.

Up and down the river
The barges go,
Up and down the darkness
River-winds blow,
And sleepers in a city
And sleepers in a town
Dream of the barges
Going up and down.

FRANCES FROST

Night Train

A train at night
is yellow lights running
across the darkness
with a sound of many
black doors slamming
in a long hall,
one after another,
but softer,
and softer,
until the last one
whispers
and closes.

ADRIEN STOUTENBURG

Santa Fe West

This is the way the wheels on the rails
rattle across a crossing
passing

a clutter of back-yard castor-bean bushes
geraniums and suddenly clattering
freight freight freight

cars and trucks on the highway
power poles striding
back back back

to a walnut orchard
and rows and rows of low
vines and wheeling spokes of citrus

back to a curve of track sweeping
away to a motionless
mountain.

This is the way the way the way
the galloping engine neighs and snorts
at the cool blue salty smell of the ocean!

HARRY BEHN

Subways Are People

Subways are people —

    People standing
    People sitting
    People swaying to and fro
    Some in suits
    Some in tatters
    People I will never know.

    Some with glasses
    Some without
    Boy with smile
    Girl with frown

    People dashing
    Steel flashing
    Up and down and 'round the town.

Subways are people —

    People old
    People new
    People always on the go
    Racing, running, rushing people
    People I will never know.

LEE BENNETT HOPKINS

Adventure

There's a place I've dreamed about far away
Where a tropical town crowds down to a bay
Busy with noise on a blowy day.

A warm mysterious coffee smell
Drifts on the air, and a singing bell
Dins and hums on a windy swell.

I've voyaged over the seven seas
In a ship that scuds before a breeze
That sounds almost like leafy trees.

When the morning is wide and windy and warm,
I watch that town from the tall yardarm
Of a poplar tree on my uncle's farm.

HARRY BEHN

SPACE AND SPACE AND SPACE...

Farther Than Far

I look into the sky and see
The leafy branches of a tree,
And higher still a bird in flight,
And higher still a cloud of white.
Beyond the cloud is lots more sky,
Farther than far, higher than high.
And where it ends, another place
Is filled with space and space and space.

MARGARET HILLERT

This Thing Called Space

It might be just beginning,
This Space,
This vacant place
Beyond Earth.

But if clouds keep rolling
White; if they keep turning gray and black,
Blowing in wind and rain and snowing and
All the Space is hidden.
How will I see it?
How will I know?

MYRA COHN LIVINGSTON

The Travelers

The moon and the satellite orbit together,
Tracing trackless circles in an endless sky,
The satellite turns to the moon in wonder
As they sail over continent, ocean and sea,
Muses over Africa, Afghanistan, Alaska,
"Can it be that I'll become ancient as she?"
Sailing South America the moon looks backward,
Skims the towering Andes with scarcely a sigh,
    "Wait, wait,
    Wait," she whispers,
    "Time is nothing
    In the endless sky."

PATRICIA HUBBELL

Two Views of the Planet Earth

1

Seen from the moon in any phase, this twisting
Earth is a green swirl of sea among
Its continents, bright in a wash of dawn

Over a desert, white where mountains rise
Out of a shadow spreading on in space;
At the pale poles the crystal ice is blue,

And all is silence as the planet drifts
About a drifting sun in blackness, carved
Of pallid color spinning, carved of light.

2

But here, beneath a crested plume of sun
The ocean is a pliant blade of waves
Carving away the coral as it grows;

Here stillness is at least a cricket song,
And everywhere the stone grows green with moss,
And ferns in their own time burst into trees,

Trees full of singing birds at dawn, and flowers,
And fragrances, and all that drifts on earth
Is a cool mist and the music of waterfalls.

HARRY BEHN

Lament for Hallowe'en

The traffic jam in outer space,
Created by the human race,
Is leaving hardly any room
For spectre's shroud or witch's broom.
The Supernatural today
Is commonplace, and phantoms say,
"There ought to be a law to clean
The heavens up for Hallowe'en."
"Spectres, unite!" they caterwaul,
"Or we will have no night at all!"

MARGARET FISHBACK

Post Early for Space

Once we were wayfarers, then seafarers,
    then airfarers;
We shall be spacefarers soon,
Not voyaging from city to city or from
    coast to coast,
But from planet to planet and from moon to moon.

This is no fanciful flight of imagination,
No strange, incredible, utterly different thing;
It will come by obstinate thought and calculation
And the old resolve to spread an expanding wing.

We shall see homes established on distant planets,
Friends departing to take up a post on Mars;
They will have perils to meet,
    but they will meet them,
As the early settlers did on American shores.

We shall buy tickets later, as now we buy them
For a foreign vacation, reserve our seat or berth,
Then spending a holiday month on a
    moon of Saturn,
Look tenderly back to our little shining Earth.

And those who decide they will not make
    the journey
Will remember a son up there or a favorite niece,
Eagerly awaiting news from the old home-planet,
And will scribble a line to catch the post for space.

PETER J. HENNIKER-HEATON

Valentine for Earth

Oh, it will be fine
To rocket through space
And see the reverse
Of the moon's dark face,

To travel to Saturn
Or Venus or Mars,
Or maybe discover
Some uncharted stars.

But do they have anything
Better than we
Do you think for instance,
They have a blue sea

For sailing and swimming?
Do planets have hills
With raspberry thickets
Where a song sparrow fills

The summer with music?
And do they have snow
To silver the roads
Where the school buses go?

Oh, I'm all for rockets
And worlds cold and hot,
But I'm wild in love
With the planet we've got.

FRANCES FROST

Solomon Grundy

Solomon Grundy
Walked on Monday
Rode on Tuesday
Motored Wednesday
Planed on Thursday
Rocketed Friday
Spaceship Saturday
Time Machine Sunday
Where is the end for
Solomon Grundy?

FREDERICK WINSOR

Message from a Mouse Ascending in a Rocket

Attention, architect!
Attention, engineer!
A message from mouse,
Coming clear:

"Suggest installing
Spike or sprocket
Easily turned by
A mouse in a rocket;
An ejection gadget
Simple to handle
To free mouse quickly
From this space-age ramble.
Suggest packing
For the next moon trip
A mouse-sized parachute
Somewhere in the ship,
So I can descend
(When my fear comes strong)
Back to earth where I was born.
Back to the cheerful world of cheese
        And small mice playing,
        And my wife waiting."

PATRICIA HUBBELL

BRIEF THOUGHTS

The Dragonfly

The dragonfly:
  his face is very nearly
  only eye.

CHISOKU

On a Journey

Wake up! Wake up! It's I
  who want you for companion
  sleeping butterfly

BASHŌ

Butterflies dancing through falling snow!
What a wonderful sight it would be.

ŌEMARU

We are forever talking
About snowmen
And yet they last
No more than a day.

NOBUYUKI YUASA

The Merry-Go-Round Horse

The merry-go-round
   horse has a tear in his eye
left by the spring rain.

One day
A horse ran fast
He ran so fast that wind
Sunlight and all the blue of day
Flew gone!

WILFORD HORNE, JR.

A leaf crashes gently to the ground
   A cricket lands lightly on it
      And tunes itself for a song.

JENNIFER HODGMAN

Little knowing
The tree will soon be cut down,
Birds are building their nests in it.

ISSA

Hope

Sometimes when I'm lonely,
Don't know why,
Keep thinkin' I won't be lonely
By and by.

LANGSTON HUGHES

A LITTLE BIT OF LAUGHTER

Phizzog

This face you got,
This here phizzog you carry around,
You never picked it out for yourself, at all, at all
— did you?
This here phizzog — somebody handed it to you
am I right?
Somebody said, "Here's yours, now go see what
you can do with it."
Somebody slipped it to you and it was like a
package marked:

"No goods exchanged after being taken away" —
This face you got.

CARL SANDBURG

Mummy Slept Late and
Daddy Fixed Breakfast

Daddy fixed the breakfast.
He made us each a waffle.
It looked like gravel pudding.
It tasted something awful.

"Ha, ha," he said, "I'll try again.
This time I'll get it right."
But what *I* got was in between
Bituminous and anthracite.

"A little too well done? Oh well,
I'll have to start all over."
That time what landed on my plate
Looked like a manhole cover.

I tried to cut it with a fork:
The fork gave off a spark.
I tried a knife and twisted it
Into a question mark.

I tried it with a hack-saw.
I tried it with a torch.
It didn't even make a dent.
It didn't even scorch.

The next time Dad gets breakfast
When Mommy's sleeping late,
I think I'll skip the waffles.
I'd sooner eat the plate!

JOHN CIARDI

The Toaster

A silver-scaled Dragon with jaws flaming red
Sits at my elbow and toasts my bread.
I hand him fat slices, and then, one by one,
He hands them back when he sees they are done.

WILLIAM JAY SMITH

Recipe

I can make a sandwich.
I can really cook.
I made up this recipe
That should be in a book:
Take a jar of peanut butter.
Give it a spread,
Until you have covered
A half a loaf of bread.
Pickles and pineapple,
Strawberry jam,
Salami and bologna
And 1/2 a pound of ham —
Pour some catsup on it.
Mix in the mustard well.
It will taste delicious,
If you don't mind the smell.

BOBBI KATZ

It's such a shock, I almost screech,
When I find a worm inside my
     peach!
But then, what really makes me
     blue,
Is to find a worm who's bit in two!

WILLIAM COLE

Accidentally

Once — I didn't mean to,
but that
was that —
I yawned in the sunshine
and swallowed a gnat.

I'd rather eat mushrooms
and bullfrogs' legs,
I'd rather have pepper
all over my eggs

than open my mouth
on a sleepy day
and close on a gnat
going down that way.

It tasted sort of salty.
It didn't hurt a bit.
I accidentally ate a gnat.
and that
was
it!

MAXINE W. KUMIN

Money

Workers earn it,
Spendthrifts burn it,
Bankers lend it,
Women spend it,
Forgers fake it,
Taxes take it,
Dying leave it,
Heirs receive it,
Thrifty save it,
Misers crave it,
Robbers seize it,
Rich increase it,
Gamblers lose it . . .
I could use it.

RICHARD ARMOUR

from The Math Battle

Cubes are swirling through my head,
Pi's attack me in my bed.
How much to carry? How much to keep?
Circles everywhere, radii too
In my brain — a number zoo!

STEPHEN SILBERAM

Valentine

I got a valentine from Timmy
Jimmy
Tillie
Billie
Nicky
Micky
Ricky
Dicky
Laura
Nora
Cora
Flora
Donnie
Ronnie
Lonnie
Connie
Eva even sent me two
But I didn't get *none* from you!

SHELLEY SILVERSTEIN

85

Macavity: The Mystery Cat

Macavity's a Mystery Cat:
    he's called the Hidden Paw —
For he's the master criminal who can defy the Law.
He's the bafflement of Scotland Yard,
    the Flying Squad's despair:
For when they reach the scene of crime —
    Macavity's not there!

Macavity, Macavity, there's no one like Macavity,
He's broken every human law,
    he breaks the law of gravity.
His powers of levitation would make a fakir stare,
And when you reach the scene of crime —
    Macavity's not there!
You may seek him in the basement,
    you may look up in the air —
But I tell you once and once again,
    Macavity's not there!

Macavity's a ginger cat, he's very tall and thin;
You would know him if you saw him,
    for his eyes are sunken in.
His brow is deeply lined with thought,
    his head is highly domed;

His coat is rusty from neglect,
    his whiskers are uncombed.
He sways his head from side to side,
    with movements like a snake;
And when you think he's half asleep,
    he's always wide awake.

Macavity, Macavity, there's no one like Macavity.
For he's a fiend in feline shape,
    a monster of depravity.
You may meet him in a by-street,
    you may see him in the square —
But when a crime's discovered,
    then *Macavity's not there!*

He's outwardly respectable.
    (They say he cheats at cards.)
And his footprints are not found
    in any file of Scotland Yard's.
And when the larder's looted,
    or the jewel-case is rifled,
Or when the milk is missing,
    or another Peke's been stifled,
Or the greenhouse glass is broken,
    and the trellis past repair —
Ay, there's the wonder of the thing!
    Macavity's not there!

And when the Foreign Office find
    a Treaty's gone astray,
Or the Admiralty lose some plans
    and drawings by the way,
There may be a scrap of paper
    in the hall or on the stair —
But it's useless to investigate —
    Macavity's not there!
And when the loss has been disclosed,
    the Secret Service say:
"It *must* have been Macavity!"
    — but he's a mile away.
You'll be sure to find him resting,
    or a-licking of his thumbs,
Or engaged in doing complicated
    long division sums.

Macavity, Macavity, there's no one like Macavity,
There never was a Cat of such deceitfulness
    and suavity.
He always has an alibi, and one or two to spare:
At whatever time the deed took place —
    MACAVITY WASN'T THERE!

And they say that all the Cats
    whose wicked deeds are widely known.

(I might mention Mungojerrie,
    I might mention Griddlebone)
Are nothing more than agents
    for the Cat who all the time
Just controls their operations:
    the Napoleon of Crime!

T. S. ELIOT

Reflections Dental

How pure, how beautiful, how fine
Do teeth on television shine!
No flutist flutes, no dancer twirls,
But comes equipped with matching pearls.
Gleeful announcers all are born
With sets like rows of hybrid corn.
Clowns, critics, clergy, commentators,
Ventriloquists and roller skaters,
M.C.s who beat their palms together,
The girl who diagrams the weather,
The crooner crooning for his supper —
All flash white treasures, lower and upper.
With miles of smiles the airwaves teem,
And each an orthodontist's dream.

'Twould please my eye as gold a miser's —
One charmer with uncapped incisors.

PHYLLIS MCGINLEY

Lines on a Small Potato

Reflect upon the dinosaur,
A giant that exists no more.
Though brawny when he was alive,
He didn't manage to survive,
Whereas the unimpressive flea
Continues healthy as can be;
So do not whimper that you're small —
Be happy that you're here at all.

· MARGARET FISHBACK

Index of Titles and Authors

Index of First Lines